rockschool®

Acoustic Guitar Debut

Performance pieces, technical exercises, supporting tests and in-depth guidance for Rockschool examinations

All accompanying and supporting audio can be downloaded from: *www.rslawards.com/downloads*

Input the following code when prompted: **8ZYPUPF5NK**

For more information, turn to page 5

Acknowledgements

Published by Rockschool Ltd. © 2016
Catalogue Number RSK200020
ISBN: 978-1-910975-27-5
Initial release | Errata details can be found at *www.rslawards.com*

SYLLABUS
Syllabus written and devised by Nik Preston and Andy G Jones
Syllabus consultants: Carl Orr and James Betteridge
Arrangements by Andy G Jones, Carl Orr and James Betteridge
Supporting Tests written by Nik Preston and Andy G Jones
Syllabus advisors: Simon Troup and Jamie Humphries

PUBLISHING
Fact Files written by Diego Kovadloff
Music engraving and book layout by Simon Troup and Jennie Troup of Digital Music Art
Proof reading and copy editing by Diego Kovadloff, Carl Orr, Mary Keene and Emily Nash
Cover design by Philip Millard
Cover photograph © REX Shutterstock

AUDIO
Produced by Nik Preston, Andy G Jones, Carl Orr and James Betteridge
Engineered by Andy G Jones, Carl Orr, James Betteridge, Jonas Persson and Music Sales
Mixed by Ash Preston, Andy G Jones, Carl Orr and James Betteridge
Mastered by Ash Preston and Paul Richardson
Supporting Tests recorded by Andy G Jones
Executive producers: John Simpson and Norton York

MUSICIANS
Andy G Jones, Carl Orr, James Betteridge, Nik Preston, Ian Thomas, Mike Finnigan, Noel McCalla,
Patti Revell, Hannah Vasanth and Jon Tatum

SPONSORSHIP
Andy G Jones endorses Thomastik Infeld strings, Providence cables and pedal switching systems, Free The Tone effects,
JJ Guitars, Ergoplay guitar supports and Wampler Pedals. All nylon strings parts recorded direct with the Yamaha NTX2000.
Carl Orr endorses MI Audio Revelation amps & effects, and Picato strings.
James Betteridge plays Martin guitars and D'addario strings.

DISTRIBUTION
Exclusive Distributors: Music Sales Ltd

CONTACTING ROCKSCHOOL
www.rslawards.com
Telephone: +44 (0)345 460 4747
Email: *info@rslawards.com*

Table of Contents

Introductions & Information

Rockschool Grade Pieces

Technical Exercises

Supporting Tests

Additional Information

Welcome to Rockschool Acoustic Guitar Debut

Welcome to **Rockschool's 2016 Acoustic Guitar syllabus**. This syllabus has been designed to equip all aspiring guitarists with a range of stylistically appropriate, industry relevant skills and a thoroughly engaging learning experience.

Utilising an array of well known repertoire and a truly crucial range of supporting tests, the continued progression of any student is assured from Debut through to Grade 8.

The syllabus has been authored to ensure that each student can develop as accompanists, soloists, sight readers and improvisers, whilst enabling both teacher and student to choose the areas that they wish to specialise in.

Rockschool's long standing commitment to raising academic standards, assessing industry-relevant skills and ensuring student engagement is world renowned. The 2016 Acoustic Guitar syllabus has been conceived in order to build upon this success and continue the evolution of the contemporary music world's first awarding body.

When combined with **Rockschool's 2015 Popular Music Theory syllabus**, this syllabus is guaranteed to furnish every candidate with both the practical skills and theoretical understanding necessary to perform at the highest level, across a whole range of contemporary repertoire.

Nik Preston – Head of Product Development and Publishing

Acoustic Guitar Exams

At each grade you have the option of taking one of two different types of examination:

- **Grade Exam**
  (Debut to Grade 5)
  A Grade Exam is a mixture of music performances, technical work and tests. You are required to prepare three pieces (two of which may be Free Choice Pieces) and the contents of the Technical Exercise section. This accounts for 75% of the exam marks. The other 25% consists of: either a Sight Reading or an Improvisation & Interpretation test (10%), two Ear Tests (10%), and finally you will be asked five General Musicianship Questions (5%). The pass mark is 60%.

  (Grades 6–8)
  A Grade Exam is a mixture of music performances, technical work and tests. You are required to prepare three pieces (two of which may be Free Choice Pieces) and the contents of the Technical Exercise section. This accounts for 75% of the exam marks. The other 25% consists of: a Quick Study Piece (10%), two Ear Tests (10%), and finally you will be asked five General Musicianship Questions (5%). The pass mark is 60%.

- **Performance Certificate**
  A Performance Certificate is equivalent to a Grade Exam, but in a Performance Certificate you are required to perform five pieces. A maximum of three of these can be Free Choice Pieces. Each song is marked out of 20 and the pass mark is 60%.

Book Contents

The book is divided into a number of sections:

- **Exam Pieces**
  Each exam piece is preceded by a Fact File detailing information about the original recording, the composer and the artist/s who performed it. There is also a Technical Guidance section at the end of each piece which provides insight from the arrangers as to the harmonic, melodic, rhythmic and technical nuance of each piece.

  Every exam piece is notated for acoustic guitar, but certain pieces feature two 'assessed' parts, meaning the candidate has the choice of which part they wish to perform in the exam. Certain pieces contain 'non-assessed' guitar parts, which are intended for duet/ensemble practice and performance. Likewise, certain pieces include notated vocal melodies in addition to the assessed guitar part. These have been included as reference material and to provide opportunity for duet and ensemble practice and performance. In your exam you must perform your pieces to the backing tracks provided.

- **Technical Exercises**
  There are either three or four types of technical exercise, depending on the grade:
  Group A – scales
  Group B – arpeggios/broken chords
  Group C – chord voicings
  Group D – a choice of stylistic studies. Please note, Group D only exists at Grades 6–8.

- **Supporting Tests**
  You are required to undertake three kinds of unprepared, supporting test:

  1. Sight Reading or an Improvisation & Interpretation test at Debut to Grade 5.
     Please note, these are replaced by mandatory Quick Study Pieces (QSPs) at Grades 6–8.

  2. Ear Tests: Debut to Grade 3 feature Melodic Recall and Chord Recognition.
     Grades 4–8 feature Melodic Recall and Harmonic Recall.

  3. General Musicianship Questions (GMQs), which you will be asked by the examiner at the end of each exam.
     Each book features examples of the types of unprepared tests likely to appear in the exam.
     The examiner will give you a different version in the exam.

- **General Information**
  You will find information on exam procedures, including online examination entry, marking schemes, information on Free Choice Pieces and improvisation requirements for each grade.

Audio

In addition to the Grade book, we have also provided audio in the form of backing tracks (minus assessed guitar part) and examples (including assessed guitar part) for both the pieces and the supporting tests where applicable. This can be downloaded from RSL directly at *www.rslawards.com/downloads*

You will need to input this code when prompted: **8ZYPUPF5NK**

The audio files are supplied in MP3 format. Once downloaded you will be able to play them on any compatible device.

You can find further details about Rockschool's Acoustic Guitar syllabus by downloading the syllabus guide from our website: *www.rslawards.com*

All candidates should download and read the accompanying syllabus guide when using this grade book.

Acoustic Guitar Notation Explained

THE MUSICAL STAVE shows pitches and rhythms and is divided by lines into bars. Pitches are named after the first seven letters of the alphabet.

TABLATURE graphically represents the guitar fingerboard. Each horizontal line represents a string, and each number represents a fret.

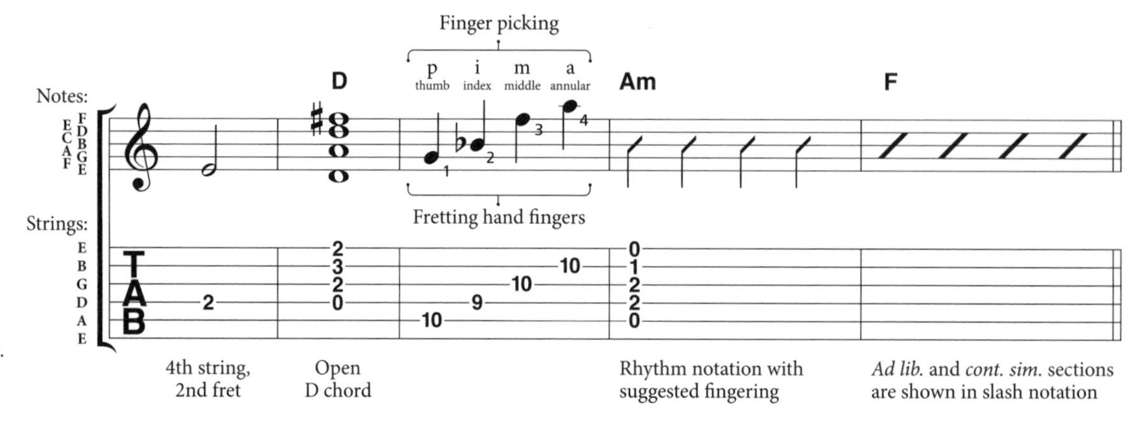

Definitions For Special Guitar Notation

HAMMER ON: Pick the lower note, then sound the higher note by fretting it without picking.

PULL OFF: Pick the higher note then sound the lower note by lifting the finger without picking.

SLIDE: Pick the first note, then slide to the next with the same finger.

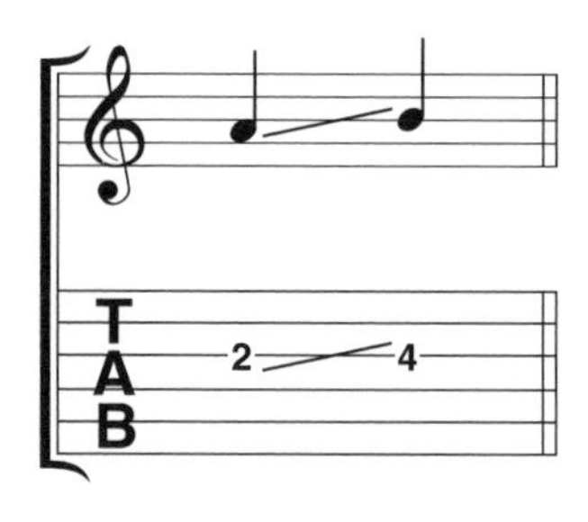

STRING BENDS: Pick the first note then bend (or release the bend) to the pitch indicated in brackets.

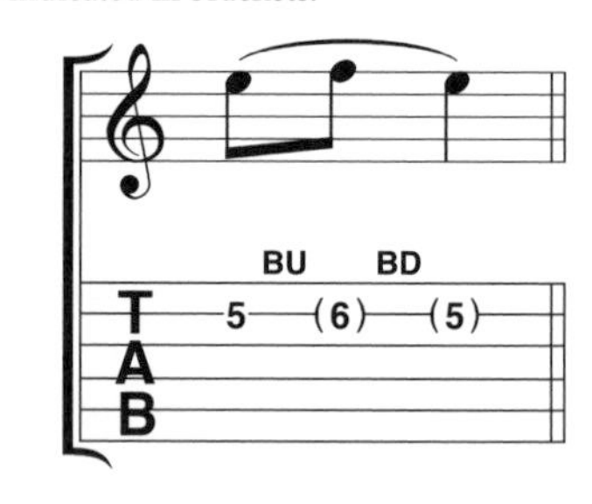

GLISSANDO: A small slide off of a note toward the end of its rhythmic duration. Do not slide 'into' the following note – subsequent notes should be repicked.

VIBRATO: Vibrate the note by bending and releasing the string smoothly and continuously.

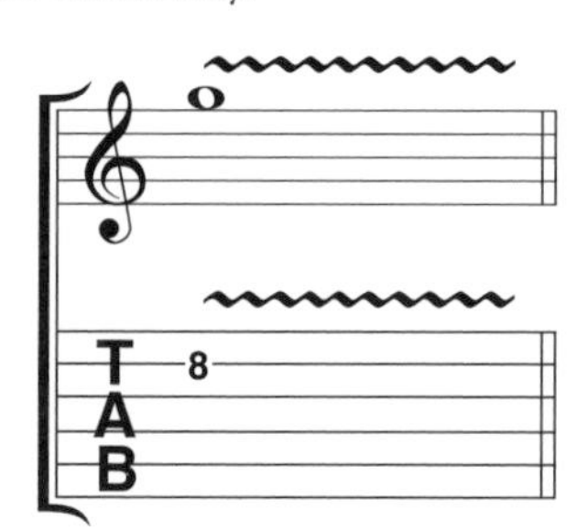

NATURAL HARMONICS: Lightly touch the string above the indicated fret then pick to sound a harmonic.

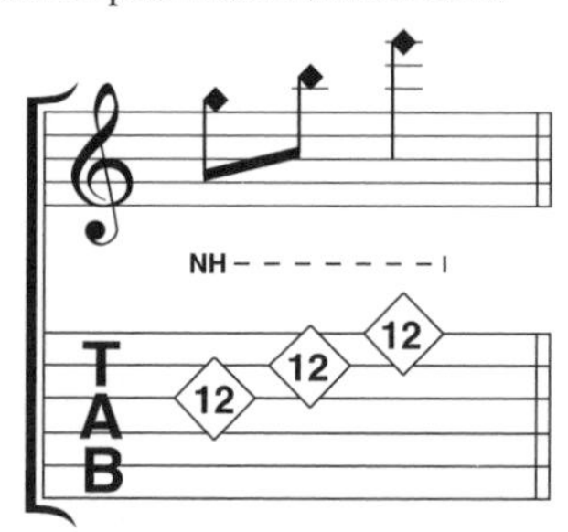

ARTIFICIAL HARMONICS: Fret the note indicated in the TAB, then (with picking hand) lightly touch the string above fret indicated between staves, and pick to sound the harmonic.

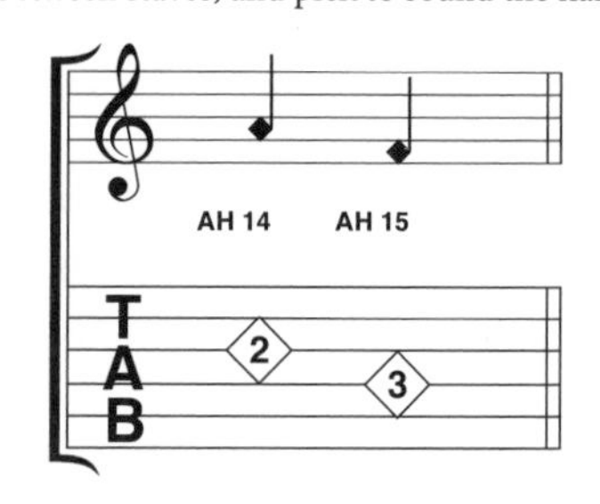

PRE-BENDS: Before picking the note, bend the string from the fret indicated between the staves, to the equivalent pitch indicated in brackets in the TAB

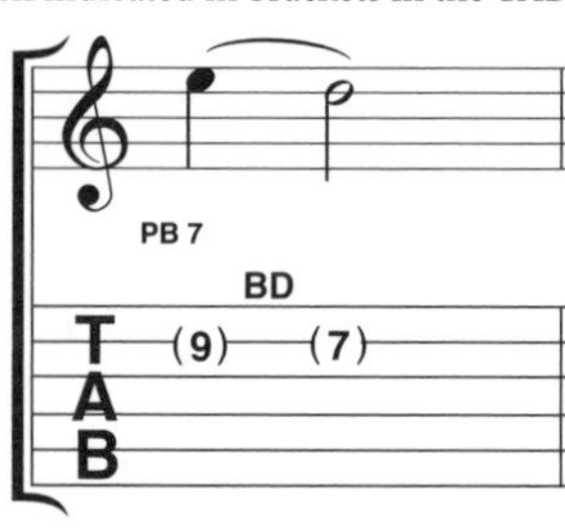

PICK HAND TAP: Strike the indicated note with a finger from the picking hand. Usually followed by a pull off.

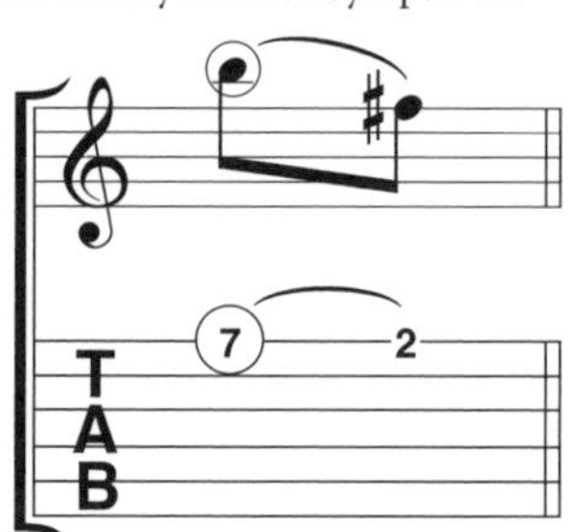

FRET HAND TAP: As pick hand tap, but use fretting hand. Usually followed by a pull off or hammer on.

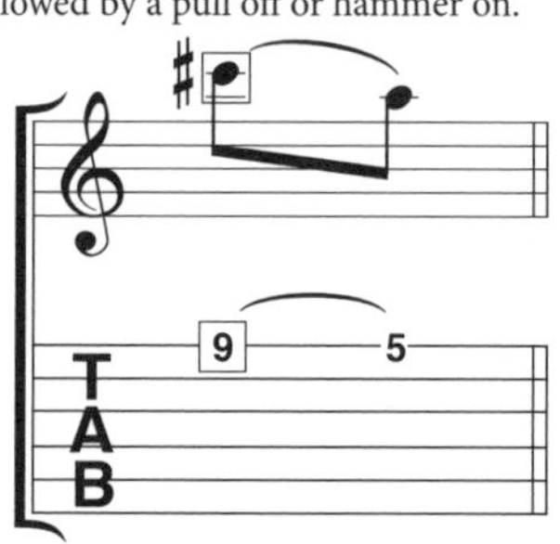

QUARTER TONE BEND: Pick the note indicated and bend the string up by a quarter tone.

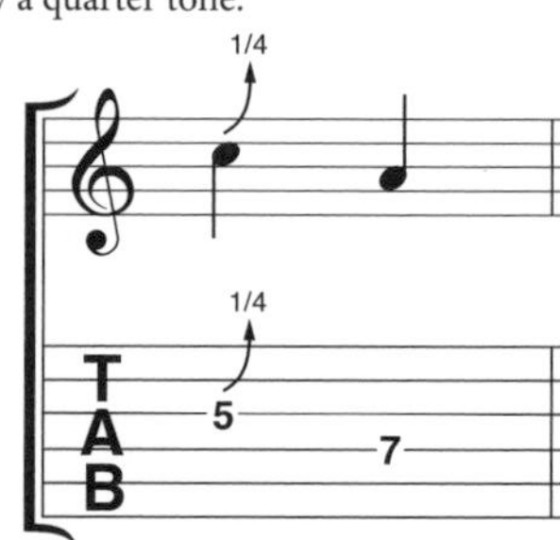

TRILL: Rapidly alternate between the two bracketed notes by hammering on and pulling off.

D.𝄋. al Coda

- Go back to the sign (𝄋), then play until the bar marked ***To Coda*** 𝄌 then skip to the section marked 𝄌 ***Coda***.

D.C. al Fine

- Go back to the beginning of the song and play until the bar marked ***Fine*** (end).

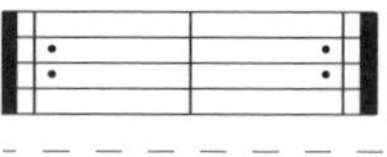

- Repeat bars between signs.

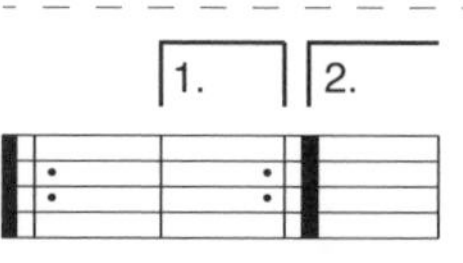

- When a repeated section has different endings, play the first ending only the first time and the second ending only the second time.

Foo Fighters | Learn To Fly

SONG TITLE: LEARN TO FLY
ALBUM: THERE IS NOTHING LEFT TO LOSE / 1999
LABEL: RCA
GENRE: HARD ROCK
WRITTEN BY: DAVE GROHL, NATE MENDEL, TAYLOR HAWKINS
GUITAR: DAVE GROHL
PRODUCER: FOO FIGHTERS AND ADAM KASPER
UK CHART PEAK: 21

'Learn to Fly' was released in 1999 and received a Grammy Award nomination for Best Performance by a Duo or Group with Vocal. It was awarded a Grammy Award for Best Music Video. The song had considerable international success and in July 2015, 1000 musicians gathered in the Italian town of Cesena to play and sing the song. A video of the event was released followed by a plea for the Foo Fighters to play in their town. It had nearly 28,000,000 views. The Foo Fighters played a concert in Cesena in November 2015 for approximately 3000 people. They opened with 'Learn to Fly'.

The album featuring 'Learn to Fly', *There is Nothing Left to Lose*, was awarded a Grammy Award for Best Rock Album in 2001. It was produced, without record company involvement, in Dave Grohl's basement in Alexandria, Virginia.

Dave Grohl is a founder member of Nirvana and Foo Fighters is the name he chose for a one man project following the death of Kurt Cobain in 1994. Grohl eventually recruited other members and Foo Fighters became a band in 1995. The Band has won four Grammy awards.

Grohl was already writing tunes during his Nirvana days but felt intimidated by Cobain's prowess. When the Foo Fighters started he borrowed elements from Nirvana's approach, such as the shift between quiet verses and loud choruses and the stripped down qualities of their songs. Grohl's riffs contain a substantial rhythmic element that relates to his drumming background. The band has developed a more sophisticated and melodic sound over the years. Grohl directed the series *Sonic Highways*, described as a 'love letter to the history of American music' where much of what influences him and the Foo Fighters is documented. Grohl also played drums with Queens of the Stone Age and in Them Crooked Vultures, featuring Led Zeppelin's John Paul Jones and Josh Homme, frontman of Queens of the Stone Age.

Learn To Fly

Foo Fighters

Arranged by Carl Orr

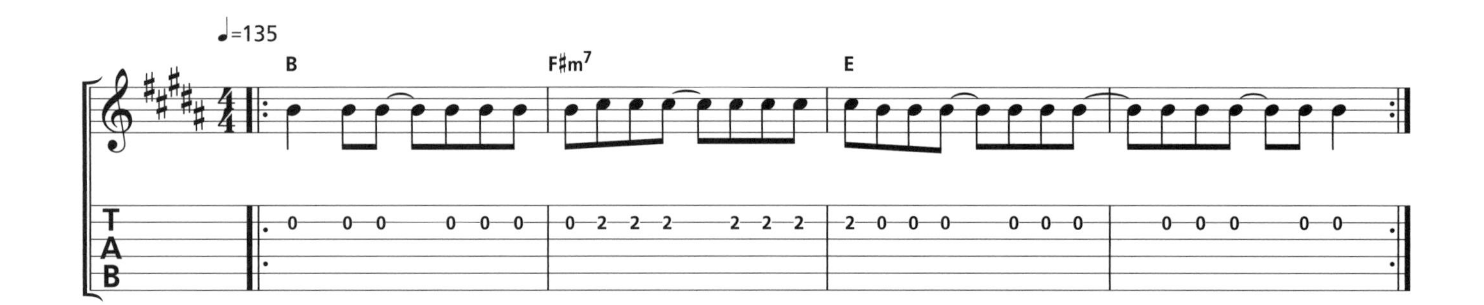

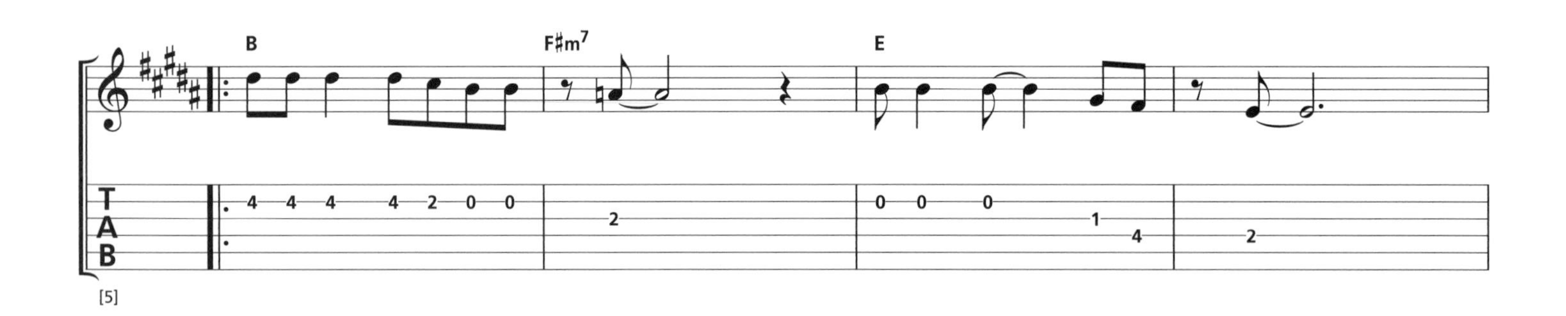

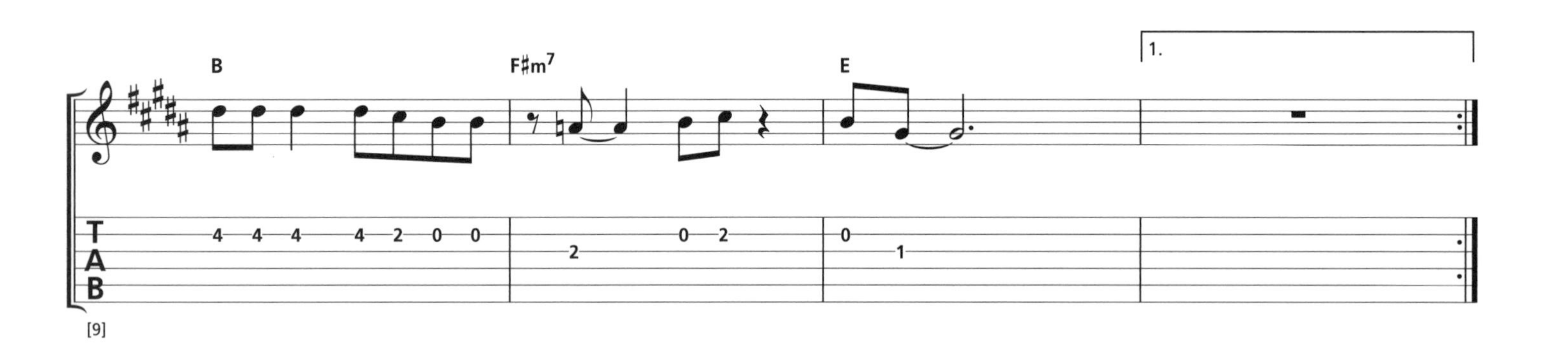

B
F♯m7
E
2 2 2 2 0 4 2
0
2 2 2 2 0 4 2
[21]

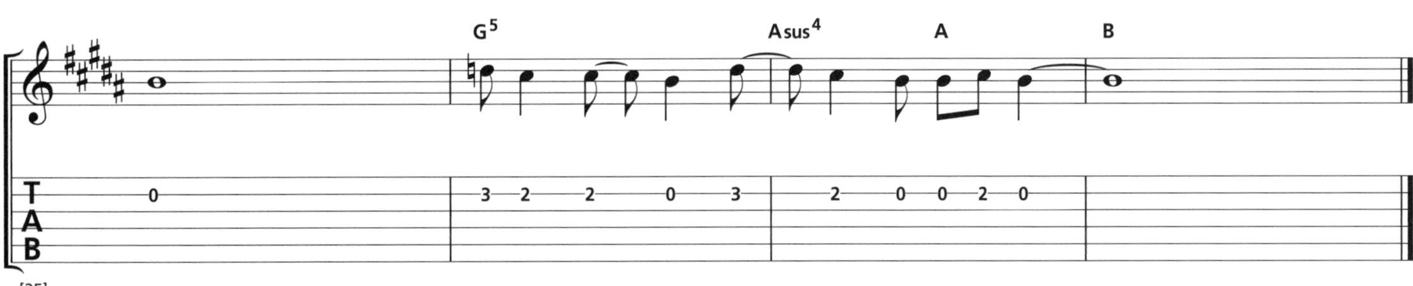
G5
Asus4
A
B
0
3 2 2 0 3
2 0 0 2 0
[25]

Learn To Fly | Technical Guidance

This classic tune encapsulates the furious style of the Foo Fighters.

While it retains the grunge from the Nirvana days, a more meticulous approach to the craft of the three minute rock song has been added. The flawless performance is clean, letting the flair, musicality and attitude of the song shine through. 'Learn to Fly' is in the key of B, which despite its close proximity to the more usual key of E, is still a relative rarity. This, however, facilitates the use of open strings and allows the full sound of the guitar to ring out. The song pulses steadily at 135 beats per minute and features a chord sequence on the B major (I/tonic), F♯minor (V/dominant) and E major (IV/subdominant) chords, repeated until bar 26, which features a cadence from the G^5 (♭VI/submediant) power chord to an $A sus^4$ (♭VII/subtonic) power chord, resolving back to the B major (I/tonic) with a great deal of drama and an element of surprise.

The intro features a very simple two note melody (B and C) which propels the song along in quavers. The verse starting at bar 5 is very simple and memorable. It's all in the low end of the neck and quite easy to play. The only tricky bit is the syncopation, such as the A note in bar 6, the phrase in bars 6 and 7 and the phrase ending in bars 10 and 11.

In bar 13, there is a slightly oddly placed pickup into the chorus starting on the and (upbeat) of 3. Also watch out for the placement of the notes in bars 18 and 19, which recurs at bars 22 and 23. The final phrase in bars 26 to 28 is also rhythmically subtle. It is best to practise each phrase individually; for example, bars 5 and 6 constitute a phrase, the musical equivalent of a small sentence. It is advisable to start by clapping the rhythm repeatedly and to play the pitches without any rhythm. Once the rhythm and pitch are secure they can slowly be combined, eventually building up to full speed.

Snow Patrol | Chasing Cars

SONG TITLE: CHASING CARS
ALBUM: EYES OPEN / 2006
LABEL: INTERSCOPE
GENRE: ALTERNATIVE ROCK
WRITTEN BY: GARY LIGHTBODY, NATHAN CONNOLLY, TOM SIMPSON, PAUL WILSON, JONNY QUINN
GUITAR: GARY LIGHTBODY AND NATHAN CONNOLLY.
PRODUCER: JACKNIFE LEE
UK CHART PEAK: 6

'Chasing Cars' is featured in Snow Patrol's 2006 release *Eyes Open*. The song gained popularity in the US, after being featured in the TV series *Grey's Anatomy*. 'Chasing Cars' sold consistently in the digital download market on both sides of the Atlantic and received a Grammy Award nomination for Best Rock Song in 2007.

The lyrics were written by singer Gary Lightbody and talk about infatuation.

In 2009, PPL announced 'Chasing Cars' was the most widely played song of the decade in the UK. The song sold nearly five million copies in the US and UK. Ed Sheeran covered it in live performances.

Snow Patrol hail from Northern Ireland and formed in 1993 at the University of Dundee.

Their first three records were released independently and did not have much commercial success. The group rose to fame with their 2005 major label release *Final Straw*. The record sold 3 million copies worldwide.

Eyes Open was released in 2006 and 'Chasing Cars' propelled the band to international fame. Snow Patrol have sold 13 million records to date. They have supported U2 and Coldplay in stadium tours.

Chasing Cars

Snow Patrol

Arranged by James Betteridge

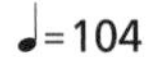

D
A
[13]
A
E/G♯
D
[17]
A
[22]

Acoustic Guitar Debut

Chasing Cars | Technical Guidance

'Chasing Cars' is in the key of A major and uses the I (tonic), IV (subdominant) and V (dominant) chords. These chords are referred to as primary chords. Harmonising the major scale will yield chords on each degree of the scale. The diagram below illustrates the diatonic chords of the A major scale.

The A major scale:

I	II	III	IV	V	VI	VII
A maj	**Bm**	**C♯m**	**D maj**	**E maj**	**F♯m**	**G♯dim**
A maj			**D maj**	**E maj**		

This version of the song has been arranged as a duet, with the first guitar playing the 8th note riff, which cycles through the chord sequence. It is important to avoid any unwanted open strings and keep the riff consistent.

In bars 17 to 24 the part switches to playing the underlying open chords. It is important to make sure all the notes in each chord can be heard clearly. The chords are notated as minims (half notes) on beats 1 and 3. Ensure the chords last for the correct duration.

The second guitar starts off playing the open chords during the intro, supporting the main riff played by guitar one. It then switches to playing the melody at the start of the bar 9. The rhythm of the melody is quite syncopated (accenting weaker parts of the beat).

For example, the melody in bar 9 starts on the 'and' (upbeat) of beat 4. This can take a little while to get used to. It is useful to practice clapping and singing the rhythm first. It is a great way to help train one's ears. Singing a line will make playing it much easier.

If the original tempo is hard to manage, it is advisable to slow it down to a comfortable speed until each section is playable. The tempo can then be gradually increased.

See note on welcome page about assessed and non-assessec

B

Gtr. 1 (Assessed)

Gtr. 2 (Assessed)

SONG TITLE: YELLOW
ALBUM: PARACHUTES
LABEL: PARLOPHONE
GENRE: POP / ALTERNATIVE ROCK
WRITTEN BY: CHRIS MARTIN, JONNY BUCKLAND, WILL CHAMPION AND GUY BERRYMAN
GUITAR: CHRIS MARTIN AND JONNY BUCKLAND
PRODUCER: KEN NELSON AND COLDPLAY
UK CHART PEAK: 4

'Yellow' is featured in Coldplay's debut album *Parachutes*. It was written whilst taking a break during the recording of the album. The band went outside of the studio to look at the stars and that inspired Chris Martin to write the lyrics. He showed them to the band and they added further lyrical and musical ideas. The song was recorded there and then.

'Yellow' received massive airplay and quickly became a popular song. By now, it is one of the band's anthems. It has been adopted by Watford FC and is played during home games.

'Yellow' was covered by Bill Frisell and Petra Haden, Sara Bareilles and Alex Parks amongst others.

Coldplay formed in 1996 whilst studying at University College London. Their quick rise to fame was accompanied by constant touring and recording. They have released seven albums to date and are a stadium filling band worldwide. Their style is rooted in melodic pop but Coldplay retain an experimental edge. As a result their sound partially changes according to the production values they apply in every new studio recording.

Coldplay have won numerous music awards, amongst them seven Grammy Awards. They have sold over 60 million records to date.

Yellow

Coldplay

Arranged by Carl Orr

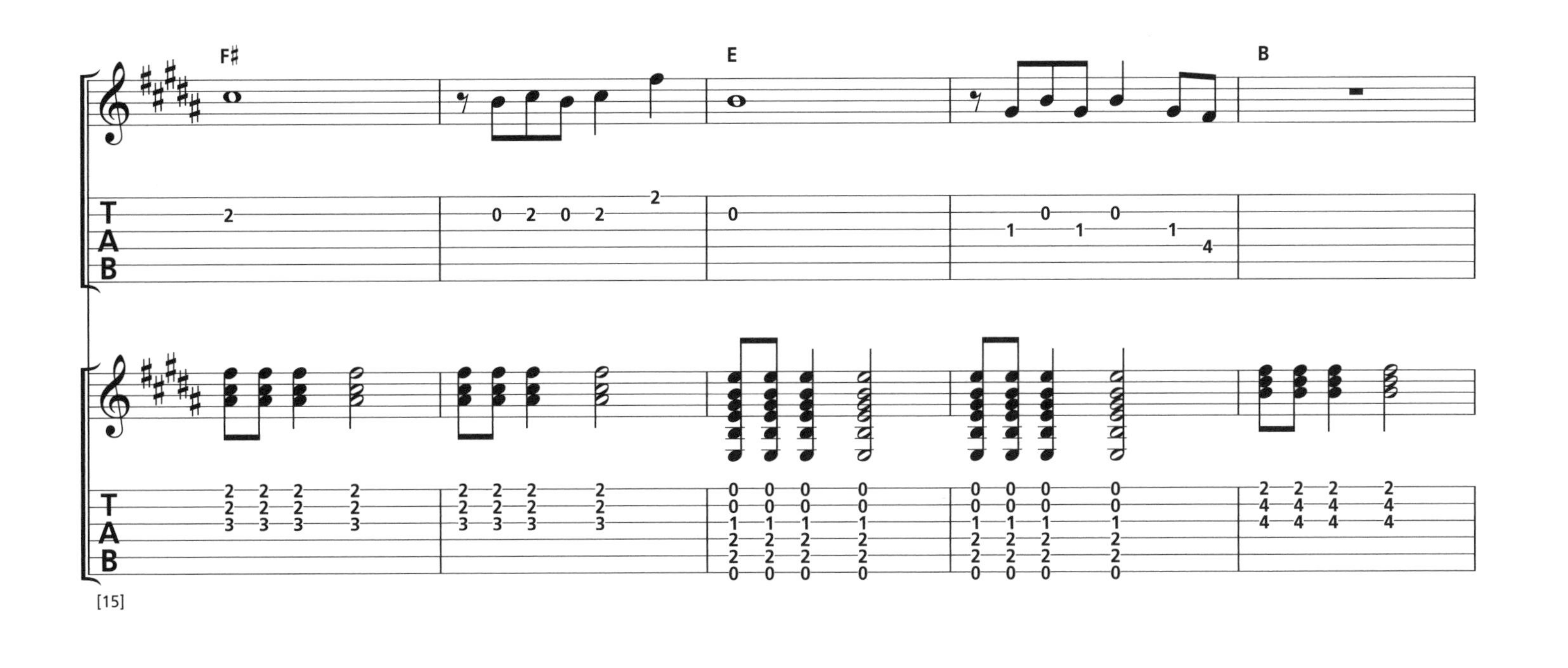
F♯
E
B
[15]

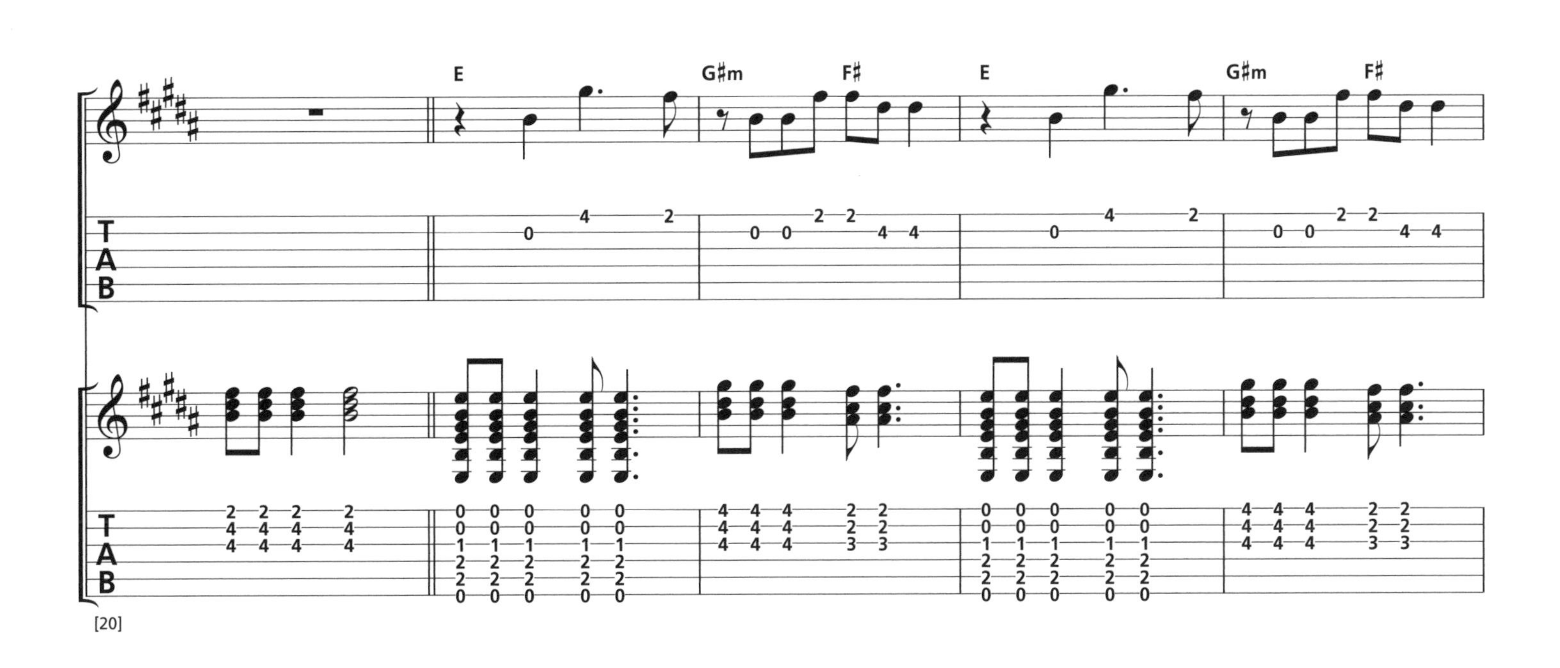
E
G♯m
F♯
E
G♯m
F♯
[20]

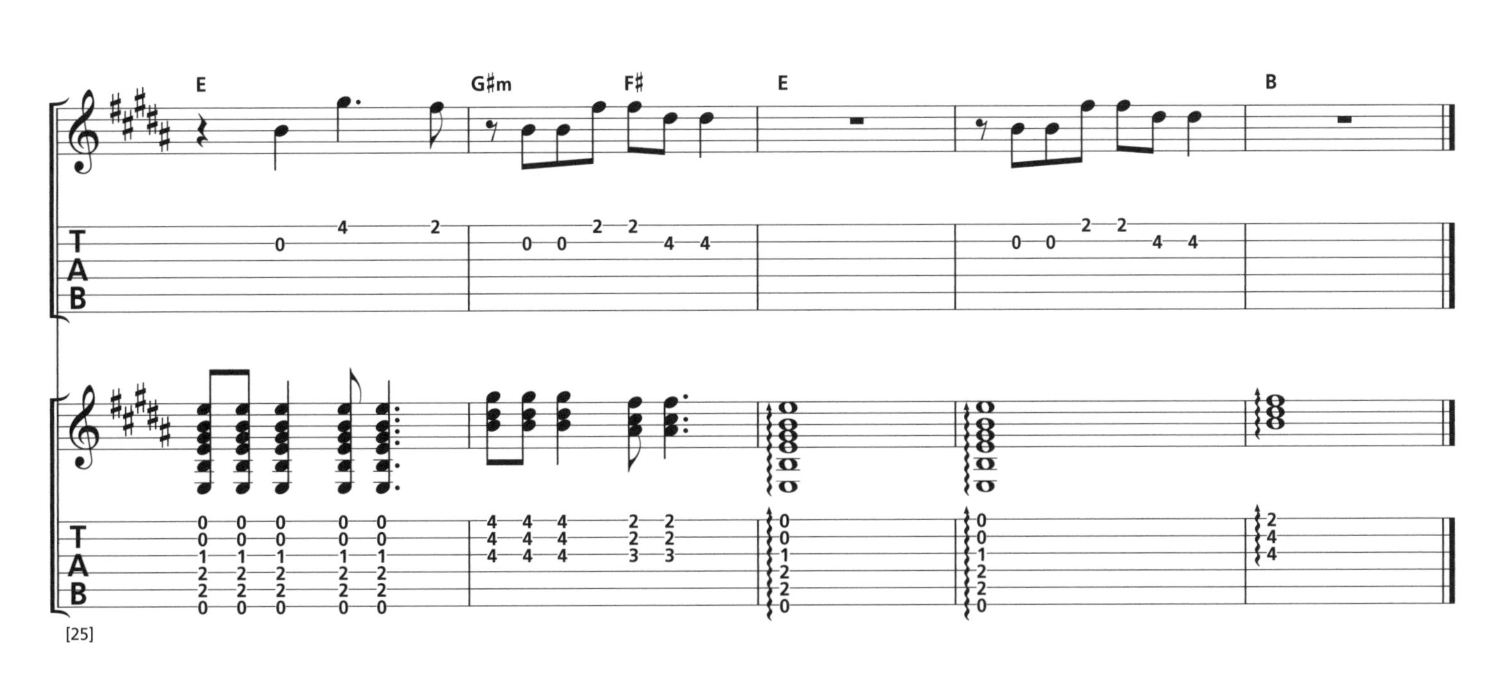
E
G♯m
F♯
E
B
[25]

Yellow | Technical Guidance

This great Coldplay song is arranged featuring chords and melody as both are playable at Debut level.

The verse consists of B major (I/tonic), F♯ major (V/dominant) and E major (IV/subdominant) played repeatedly, creating a meditative mood, with two bars on each chord, forming a 6-bar phrase. This is a slightly unusual length as most popular music is written in multiples of four bars. In the chorus, from bar 21, the mood changes by starting on the IV chord (subdominant) for one bar, followed by half a bar on the VI minor (submediant) and half a bar on the V (dominant) chord. The chords in this section are moving much faster than in the previous one, creating a feeling of urgency. The section finishes with an unresolved IV chord, creating tension resolved by the tonic in the following bar (29).

In the verse, all of the chords can be strummed with a downstroke. Alternatively, the second chord in each bar can be played with an upstroke. The chorus can be strummed with downstrokes throughout or with an upstroke on the second and last chord in each bar. It is very important to keep time steadily. It is advisable to use a metronome or tap your foot, as the constant, unwavering beat is the foundation of this song.

Most of the chord voicings are small at just three notes, to facilitate easier chord changes, except for the E major chords, which are written out in their full six-string voicing. Alternatively, only the top three strings of the E major chord can be played, to give them a similar texture to the rest of the voicings.

The melody is quite easy and can be played within the first four frets. It is a fundamental aspect of the song, so it is important to execute it clearly and confidently.

There are some subtle rhythms in the melody, such as the offbeat at the start of the line. It is advisable to clap the rhythm of each bar, then play the pitches without any rhythm, and finally combine rhythm and pitches. Playing evenly, with all the notes at approximately the same volume, will give the melody a good flow.

SONG TITLE: BROWN EYED GIRL
ALBUM: BLOWIN' YOUR MIND
LABEL: BANG
GENRE: RHYTHM AND BLUES
WRITTEN BY: VAN MORRISON
GUITAR: ERIC GALE, HUGH MCKRAKEN AND AL GORGONI.
PRODUCER: BERT BERNS
UK CHART PEAK: 60

'Brown Eyed Girl' was released as a single in 1967 and it has become a staple of the classic rock genre. It is still played on radios worldwide and is covered by many acts all over the world. 'Brown Eyed Girl' has been played in excess of 11 million times on US radio alone. The song was recorded as part of an eight track session with the intention of releasing four singles. Van Morrison, apparently, has not received any royalties for the song. This is addressed in the lyrics to 'The Big Royalty Check'. Van Morrison does not regard 'Brown Eyed Girl' as one of his best songs. Despite this, the single served as a catalyst to relaunch his career after leaving the Belfast band Them and relocating to the United States, where he subsequently signed to Warner Bros and recorded his career-defining *Astral Weeks*.

The original title of the song was 'Brown Skinned Girl' and had a Jamaican Calypso feel. The title was subsequently changed to 'Brown Eyed Girl'.

George Ivan Morrison was born in Belfast in 1945. He played a variety of instruments from a young age. He rose to prominence as the lead singer of Them, with whom he recorded the garage band classic 'Gloria'. *Astral Weeks* and *Moondance*, recorded in 1968 and 1970 respectively, cemented his career in the early 1970s. His legendary live performances continue captivating audiences to this day. He blends soul and R&B with folk and Celtic influences in a highly personal fashion. Van Morrison was knighted and inducted into the Songwriter's Hall of Fame in 2015.

Brown Eyed Girl

Van Morrison

Arranged by Andy G Jones

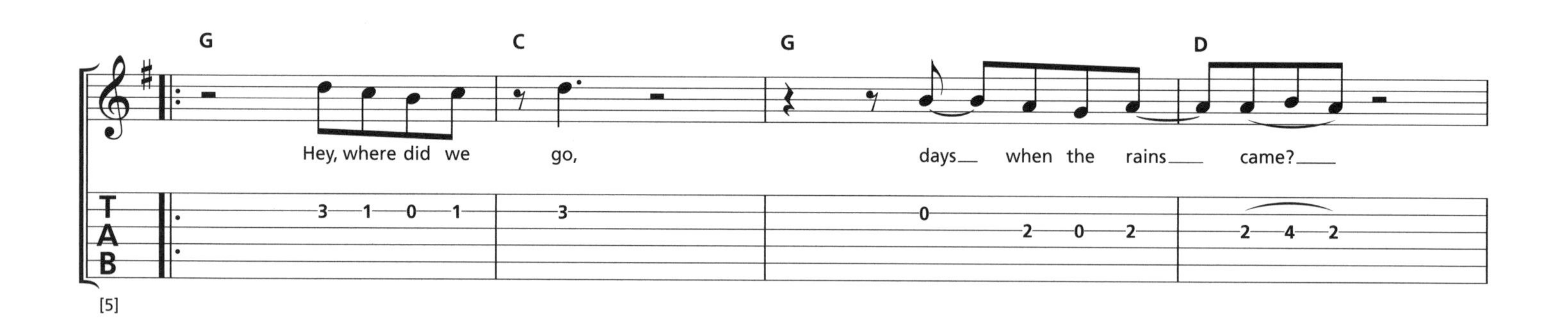

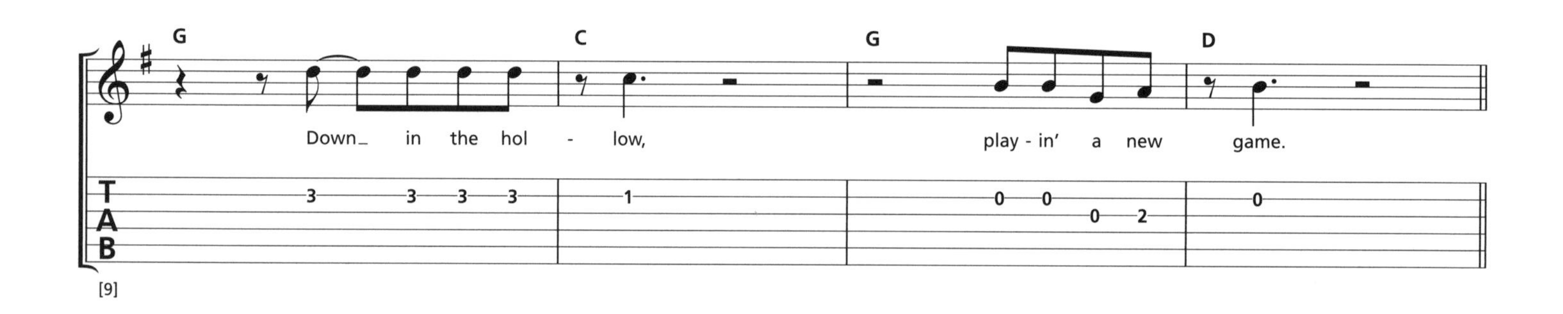

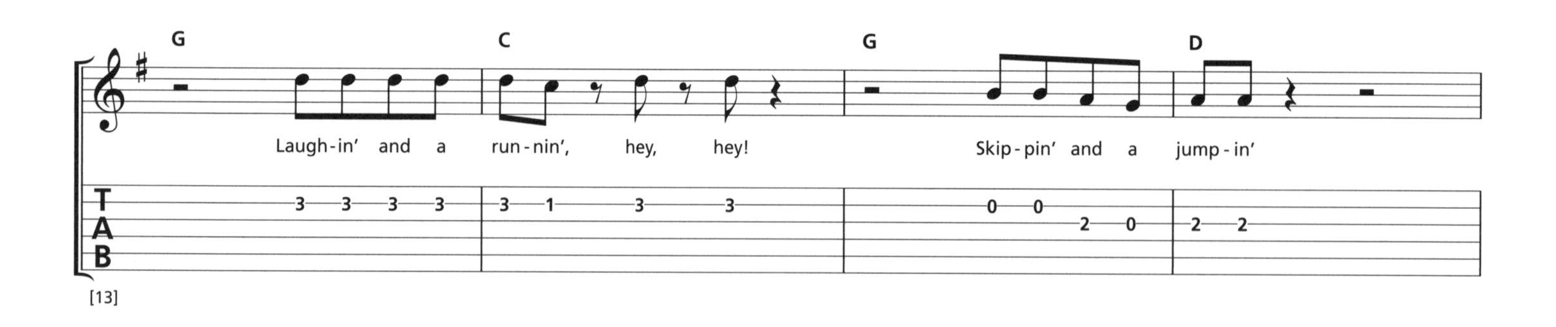

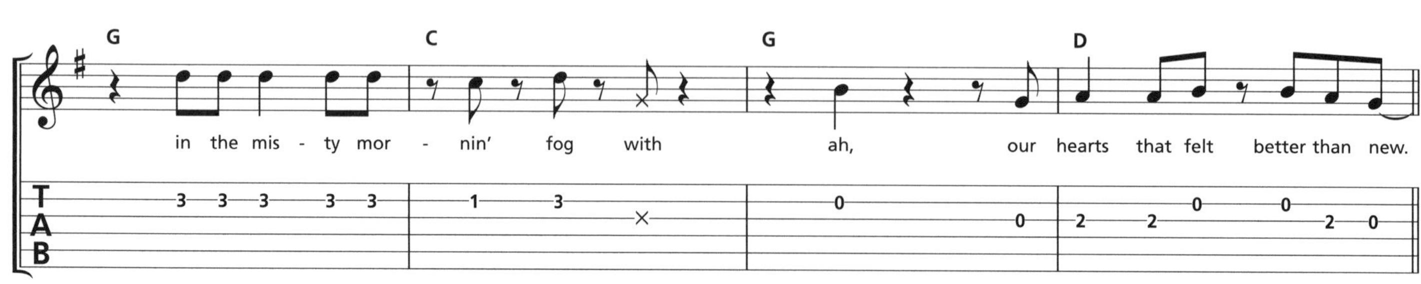

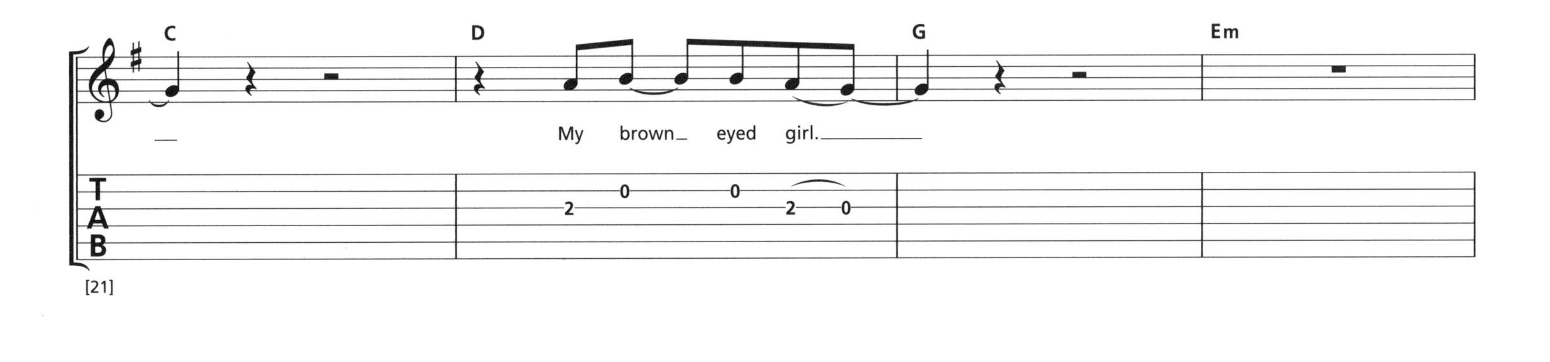
C D G Em
My brown eyed girl.
[21]

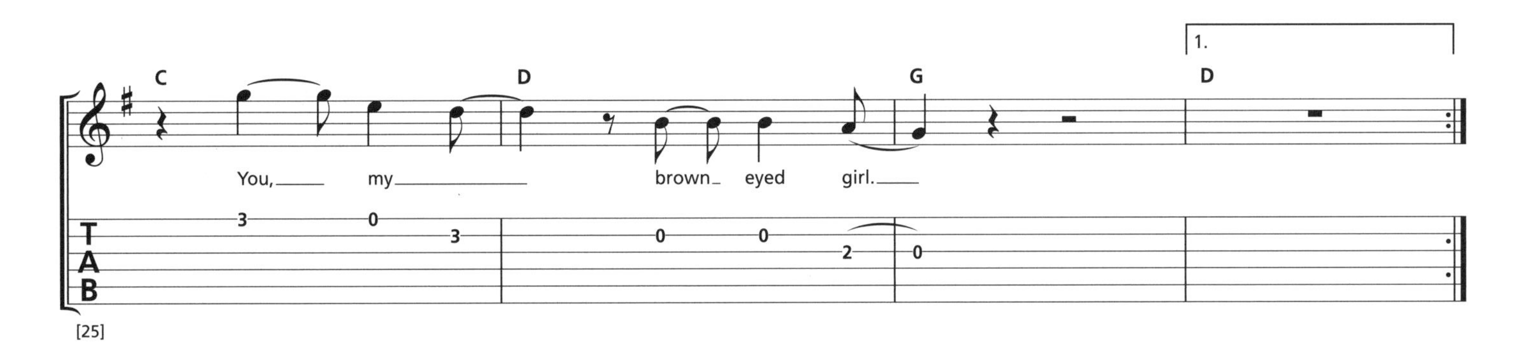
1.
C D G D
You, my brown eyed girl.
[25]

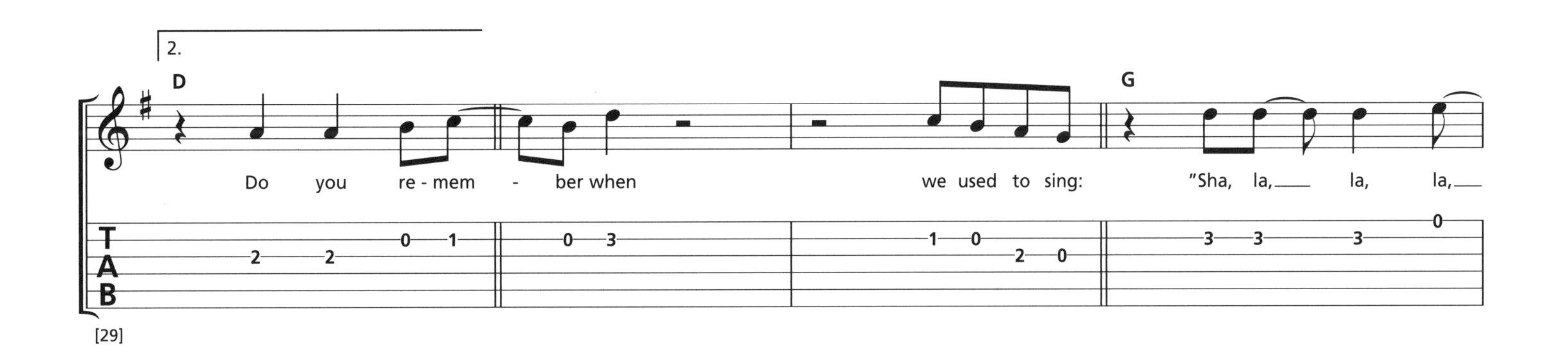
2.
D G
Do you re - mem - ber when we used to sing: "Sha, la, la, la,
[29]

C G D G
la, la, la, la, la, la, la te, da. Sha, la la, la,
[33]

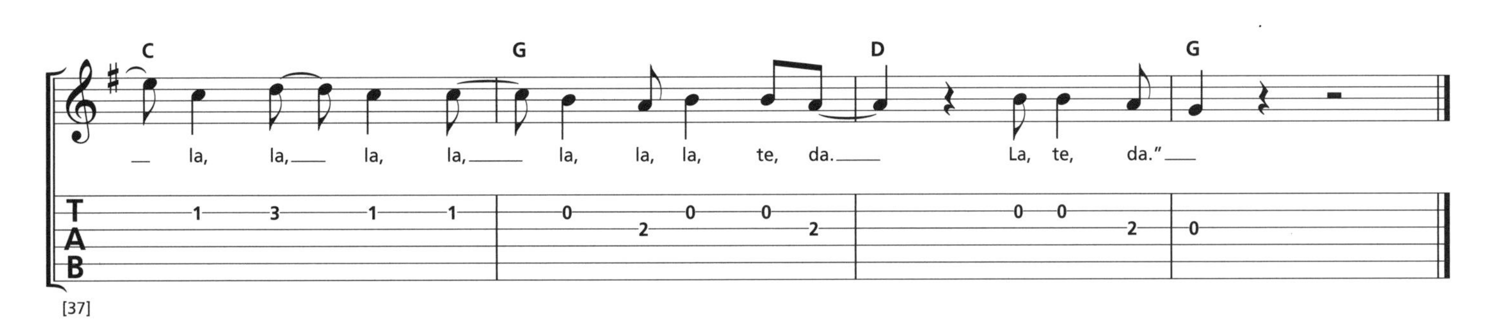
C G D G
la, la, la, la, la, la, la, te, da. La, te, da."
[37]

Brown Eyed Girl | Technical Guidance

This arrangement of Brown Eyed Girl is presented as a melody. Use your right hand fingers, pure fingerstyle or hybrid picking, which is where you hold the pick normally but also use the other available fingers to pick the strings as well. This is an approach prevalent amongst country guitar players.

The Belfast Telegraph stated that according to Morrison, the single, released in mid-June 1967, was originally entitled Brown Skinned Girl. Remarking on the original title, he said: "That was just a mistake. It was a kind of Jamaican song… Calypso". This is quite enlightening as it sheds some light on the inspiration for the rhythm guitar part. It really does have something of the calypso feel (it also sounds a little like a South African Township groove).

The guitar intro is written as a cue only and is not required for the exam. As you get more proficient this part might be worth learning, it sets the pace for the whole song. This tune is a covers/party band classic.

Note that the rhythm of the melody's first phrase (bars 5 and 6) is repeated three times. The next section does the same thing – a motif in bars 13 and 14 is repeated with some variations in the next six bars. Repetition is typical of Van Morrison's compositions and may, in part, explain his huge popularity. It is a device common in the structure of the classic 12 bar blues where a simple melodic phrase (typically a four bar phrase) is repeated two or three times to complete the structure.

There is plenty of syncopation in the song. Many notes landing off the beat add variety to the rhythm of a melody. Whilst these rhythms may seem difficult at first, you should be aware that you're learning a vital part of the musical puzzle that will enfold as you continue your studies. Rhythms can often be seen as a combination of set pieces that make up a whole. When students start to study funk rhythm guitar it is best to break rhythms down to basic units comprised of the obvious subdivisions of the bar. This piece can be regarded as an early glimpse into the process of rhythmic studies.

The 'Sha-La-La' section at the end is also heavily syncopated with many notes falling on the off beat. It is also distinguished by the use of tied notes that give the music a sort of bounce. This is another element that may have contributed to the popularity of the song.

The harmony, as with most of Van Morrison's output is very diatonic - it stays firmly within the home key of G major.

SONG TITLE: IF I WERE A BOY
ALBUM: I AM...SASHA FIERCE
LABEL: COLUMBIA
GENRE: POP
WRITTEN BY: BC JEAN AND TOBY GAD
GUITAR: REGGIE SYIENCE PERRY
PRODUCER: BEYONCE AND TOBY GAD
UK CHART PEAK: 1

'If I Were A Boy' was written by BC Jean and Toby Gad. The lyrics were written by BC Jean and are based on the break up of a romantic relationship. The idea behind the title is to try and see things from the perspective of the male in the relationship whilst pondering what would be different if he had a woman's sense of empathy.

'If I Were A Boy' is the only song in the album *I Am... Sasha Fierce* that Beyoncé did not co-write. The song was also recorded in Spanish and released as a single in Mexico and Spain.

Beyoncé Knowles was born in Houston, Texas, in 1981. She performed and sang from a young age and in the late 1990's rose to fame as the lead singer of R&B girl group Destiny's Child, with whom she sold 60 million records. Beyoncé has a four octave vocal range and her voice and singing style are distinctive and powerful.

During a break with the band in 2003 she released *Dangerously in Love*. The record was an immediate success, selling 12 million copies and earning five Grammy Awards. Her solo career continued to grow and she has now sold an approximate 120 million records.

Beyoncé is one of the best selling artists of all time and is the most nominated woman in the Grammy Awards history. She has won 20 Grammys.

Her lyrics are mainly related to themes of love, relationships and female empowerment. She is regarded as a modern day feminist icon. Her shows are highly choreographed and draw massive audiences worldwide. She is also an actress, with credits such as The Pink Panther and Dreamgirls. Beyoncé is married to rap superstar Jay Z.

If I Were A Boy

Beyoncé

Arranged by James Betteridge

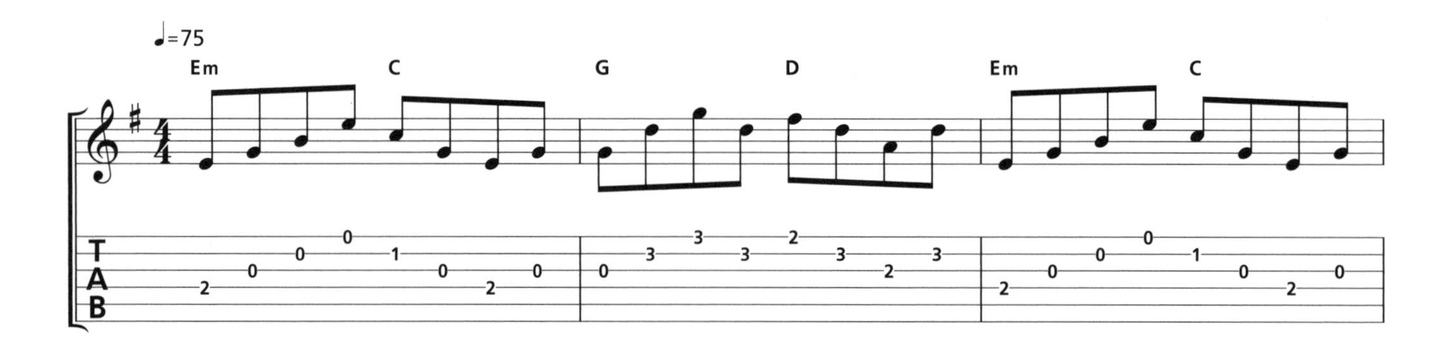

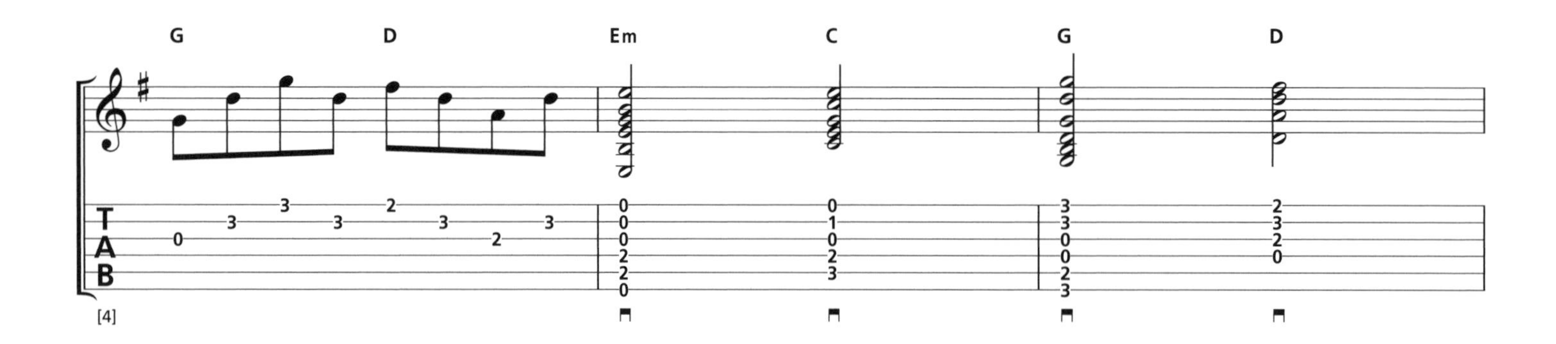

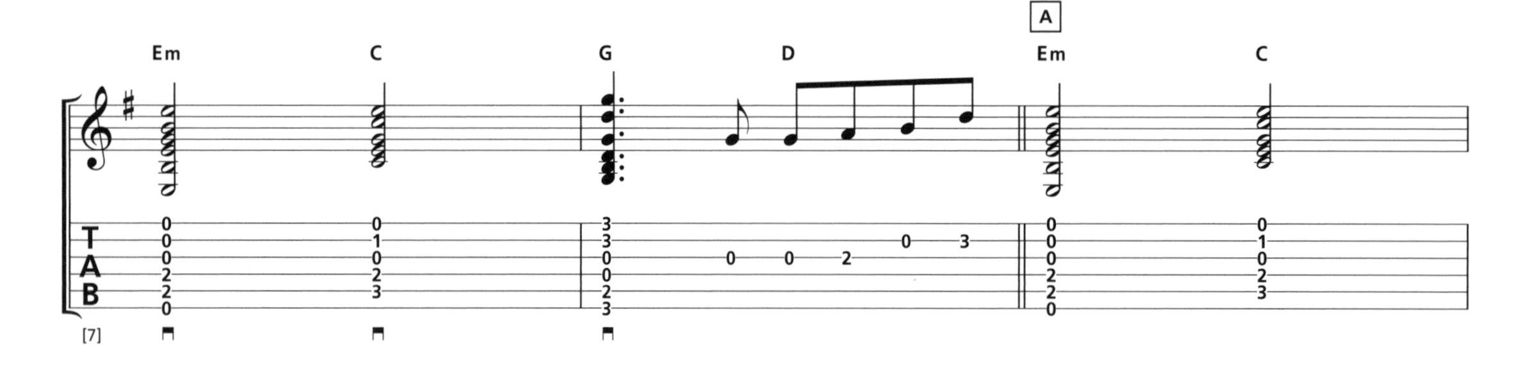

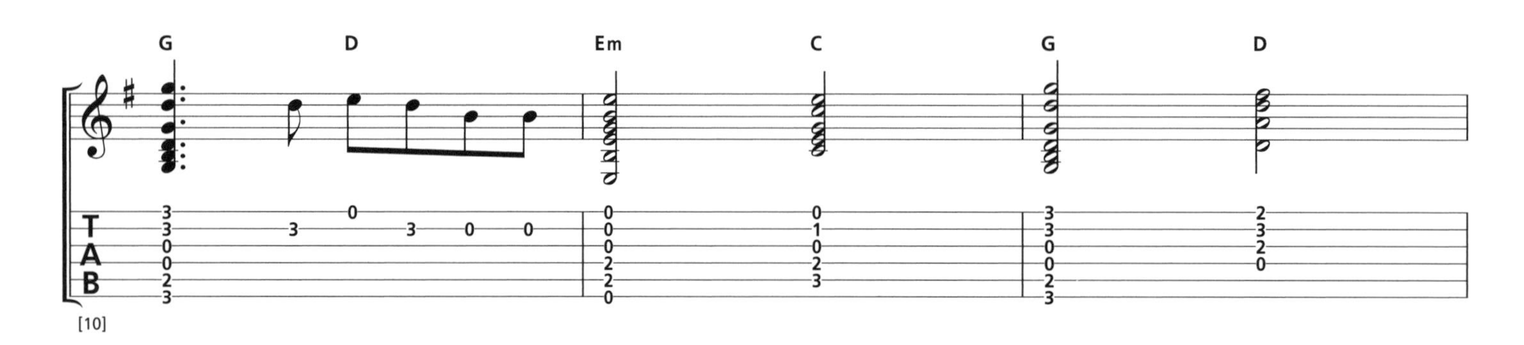

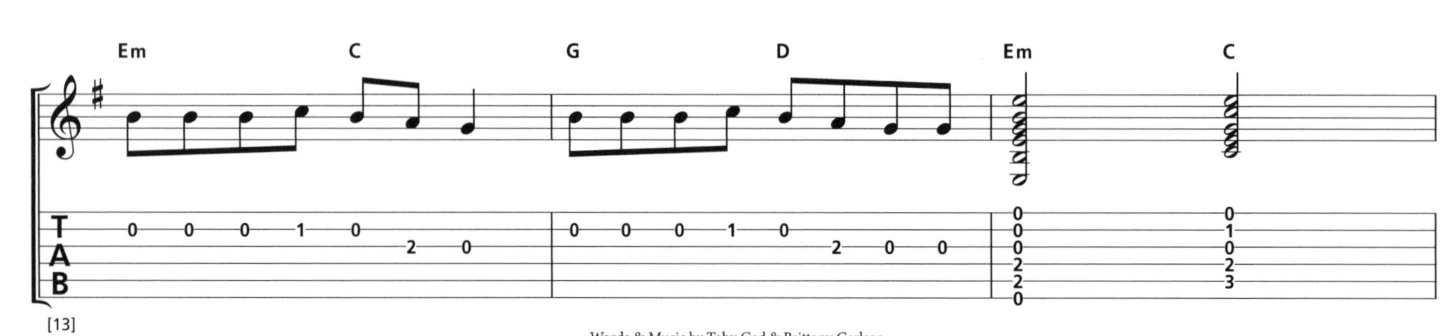

Acoustic Guitar Debut

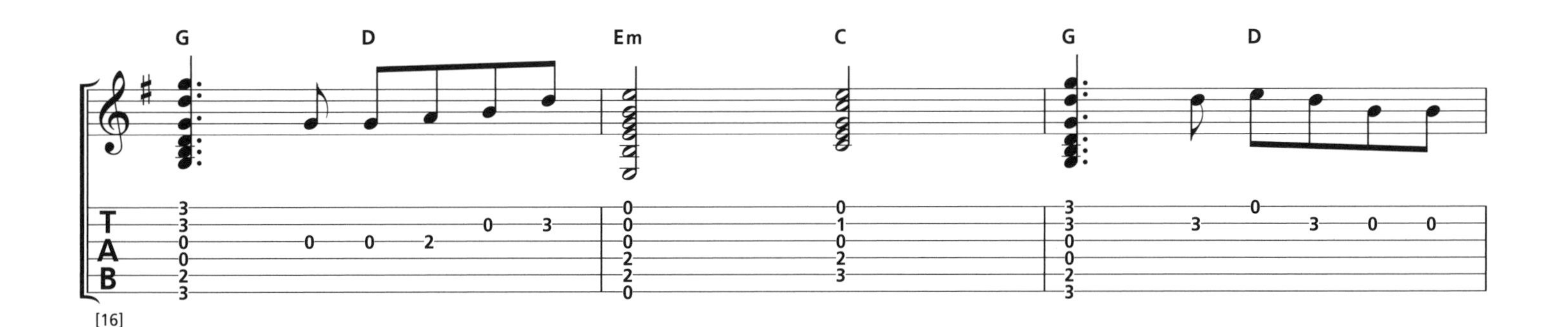
G D Em C G D
[16]

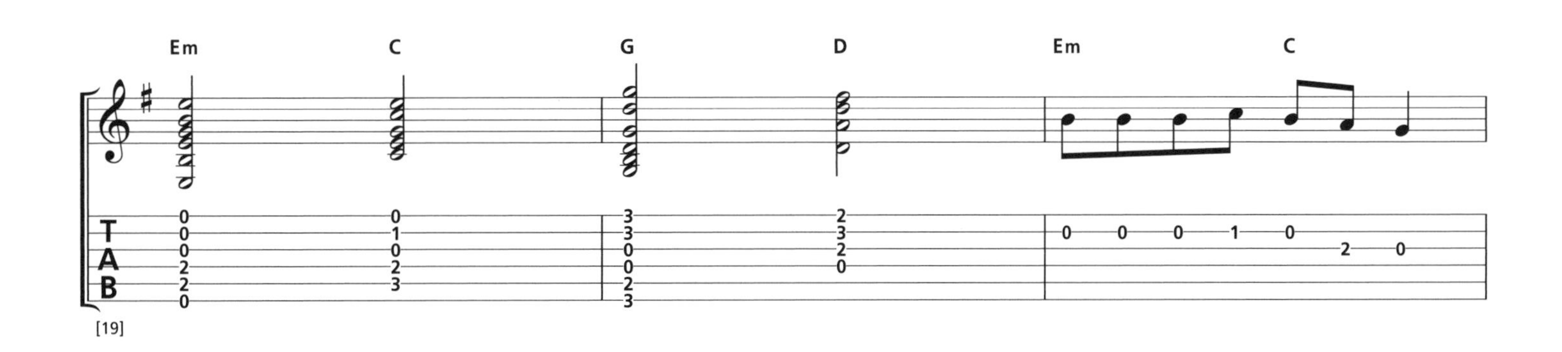
Em C G D Em C
[19]

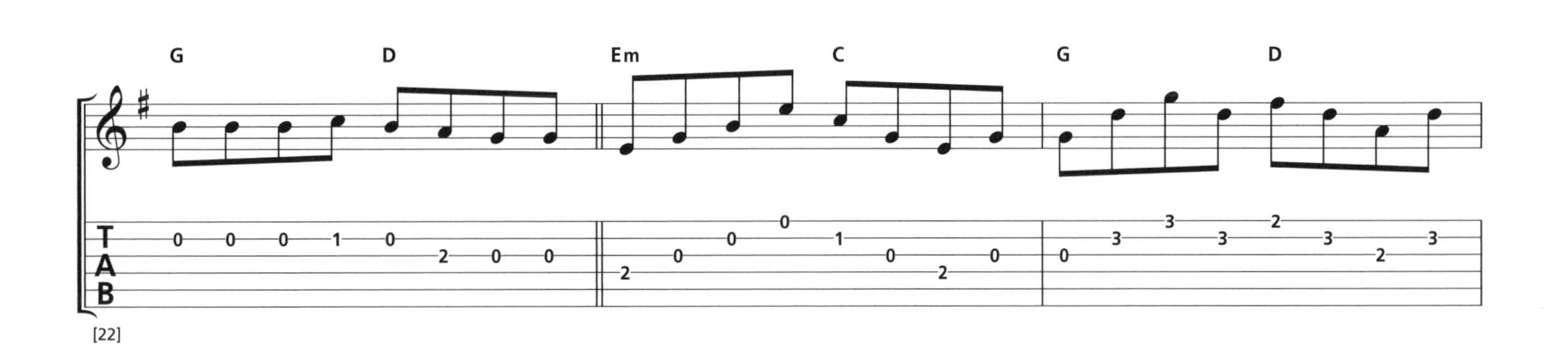
G D Em C G D
[22]

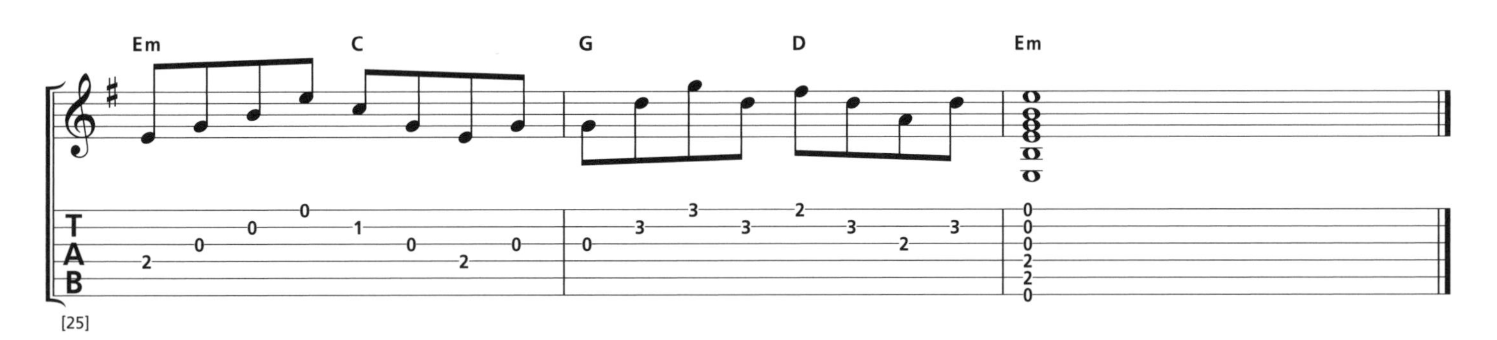
Em C G D Em
[25]

If I Were A Boy | Technical Guidance

'If I Were A boy' is in the key of E minor, and cycles around E minor (I/tonic), C major (♭VI/submediant), G major (♭III/ mediant) and D major (♭VII/subtonic).

The diagram below illustrates where each chord belongs within the key. Notice each degree of the scale is numbered with a roman numeral. Roman numerals allow musicians to quickly identify the chord progression in a piece of music.

The E natural minor scale:

I	II	♭III	IV	V	♭VI	♭VII
Em	F♯dim	G maj	A min	B min	C maj	D maj
Em		G maj			C maj	D maj

This abridged arrangement contains the intro and chorus from the original song. It starts with an 8th note arpeggiated pattern that outlines the chords in the progression. It is advisable to slow the tempo down to begin with and once the arpeggios are comfortable the tempo can be raised up to speed.

The chorus (Bars 9–21) combines chords and the melody together. Take note of the suggested strumming pattern notated above the tablature. It is important to make sure that all of the notes in the chords are heard clearly and last for the correct duration. The melody is made up of notes from the E minor scale and is a good exercise for playing melodies in open position. It is advisable to practise the chords and melody separately before piecing them together.

The chord to melody transitions ought to be as smooth as possible and without hesitation. Playing along with a metronome is a good test.

The song ends with a recap of the arpeggiated intro figure. Aim for a legato (smooth) sound, letting each note ring into the next.

Bob Marley | No Woman, No Cry

SONG TITLE: NO WOMAN, NO CRY
ALBUM: NATTY DREAD / 1974
LABEL: ISLAND
GENRE: REGGAE
WRITTEN BY: VINCENT FORD
GUITAR: BOB MARLEY, JUNIOR MARVIN AND AL ANDERSON
PRODUCER: BOB MARLEY AND CHRIS BLACKWELL
UK CHART PEAK: 22

'No Woman, No Cry' is credited to Vincent Ford, who ran a soup kitchen in Kingston, Jamaica. Marley sent him the royalty payments accrued from the song and that ensured the survival and continual running of the soup kitchen.

It was originally recorded for Island Records by Pete Tosh in 1973 but that recording remains unreleased. The song's lyrics are about life in the Ghetto and about persuading a woman that things will get better, asking her not to cry.

The Wailers recorded it in 1974 and featured it in *Nutty Dread*. It was recorded again, live at London's Lyceum Theatre in 1975, during the promotional tour of *Nutty Dread*. These versions brought the tune to mass audiences and remain very popular worldwide. The live version is included in the Rolling Stone magazine 500 Greatest Songs of All Time.

The song has been covered numerous times, by The Fugees, Nina Simone, Joan Baez, Pearl Jam, Whoopi Goldberg and Graham Parker amongst many others.

Bob Marley and The Wailers are a highly influential band. Bob Marley has risen to become a cult figure since his death in 1981, at the young age of 36. Jamaican culture and identity are, to many, intimately linked to him. He was born in 1945 and started playing music at a young age. In 1963 he formed The Wailers with Neville Livingston (Bunny Wailer) and Pete Tosh.

Marley was a committed Rastafarian whose gentle personality, politically and socially conscious lyrics and gift for songwriting made an explosive mix when coupled with the reggae flavour of his native Jamaica. His music gained worldwide appeal in the 70's, particularly after the release of *Exodus* in 1977.

Marley was the subject of an assassination attempt in 1976. He was diagnosed with cancer in 1977 and died from the disease in May 1980 whilst promoting *Uprising*. His music's popularity has continued to grow since.

His life has been the subject of many books and documentaries. Marley fathered eleven children.

No Woman, No Cry

Bob Marley

Arranged by Andy G Jones

Words & Music by Vincent Ford

C G/B Am F C G/B
O-ba, o-ba - ser - ving the hy - po-crites as they would min-gle with the good peo - ple we
[34]
Am F C G/B Am F
meet. No, wo - man, no cry.
[40]
C F Em Dm C C G/B
No, wo - man, no cry.
Here lit-tle dar - lin',
[46]
Am F C F Em Dm C
don't shed no tears. No, wo-man, no cry.
[52]
C G/B Am F C
Ev - 'ry-thing's gon - na be al - right. Ev - 'ry-thing's gon - na be al - right. Ev - 'ry-thing's gon - na
[58]
1. 2.
G/B Am F F C
be al - right. Ev - 'ry-thing's gon - na be al - right. be al - right. No, wo - man no cry.
[63]

Acoustic Guitar Debut

No Woman, No Cry | Technical Guidance

The Wailers' style fuses authentic reggae with a sophisticated American influenced soul/R&B sensibility. This melody seems pretty simple, but upon listening to the way that Bob Marley sings it, it will become apparent how much good phrasing can bring to the music.

Listen to the backing track and ensure the delivery is in time with the groove. There is room to be quite lyrical with the way the melody is stated. It can be played either fingerstyle or with a pick.

The arrangement starts with an intro that outlines the harmony above the classic descending bassline.

If holding these chords down is painful for your left hand, be careful not to strain your hand by practising this section for too long. As soon as you feel tension, get up walk around, shake your arms out, even take a little break. If you keep working on it, your strength will quickly improve.

Be careful when first preparing this piece to adhere to the rhythm on the page. If you learn the melody by playing along with Bob Marley's beautiful version, you'll be pulled into some complicated rhythms that would not have been appropriate to include in this book at this level.

Technical Exercises

In this section, you will be asked to play a selection of exercises, chosen by the examiner, from each of the groups below.

All exercises need to be played in straight feel, in the keys, octaves and tempos shown. You may use your book for Group A and Group B. All Group C exercises must be played from memory.

Note that Groups A and B need to be played to a click and any fingerings shown are suggestions only.

Group A: Scales

The tempo for this group is ♩=52 bpm.

1. C major scale | Ascending first

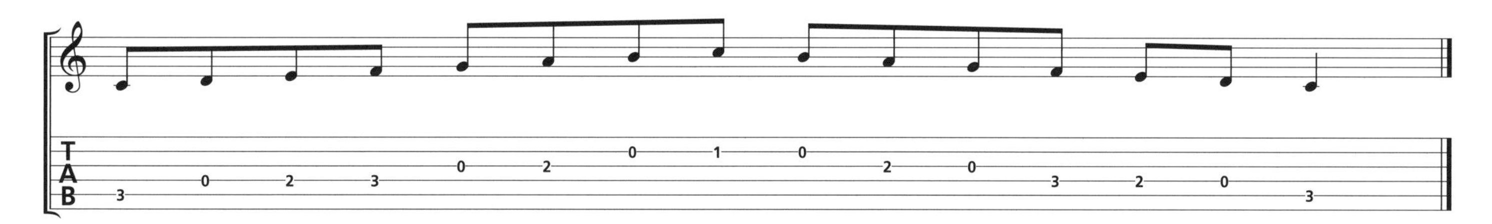

2. C major scale | Descending first

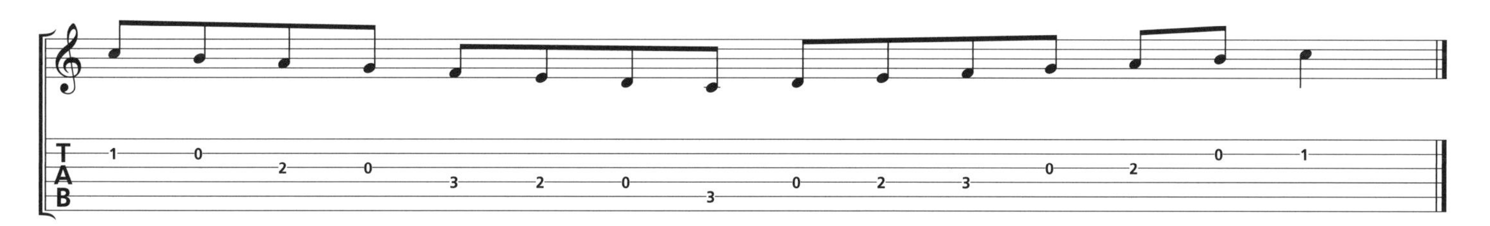

3. A natural minor scale | Ascending first

4. A natural minor scale | Descending first

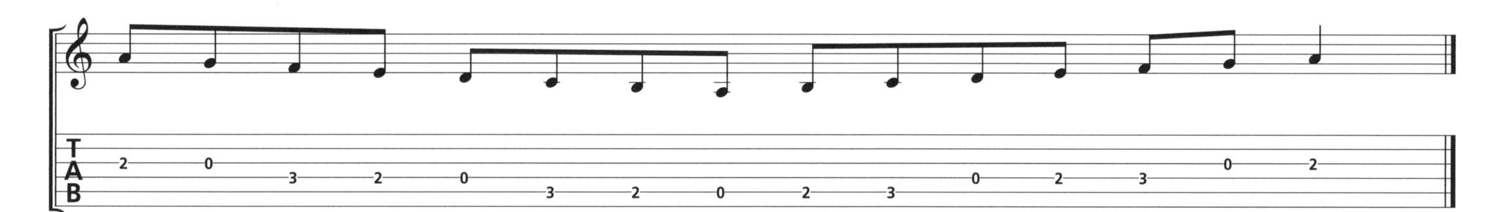

Group B: Arpeggios

The tempo for this group is ♩=92 bpm.

1. C major arpeggio

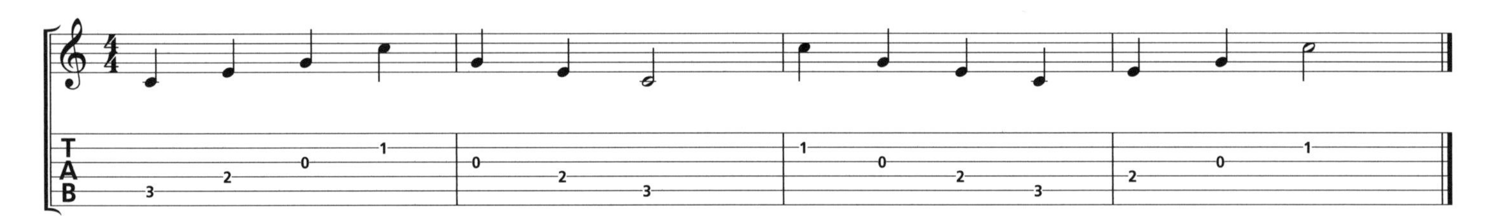

2. C major arpeggio

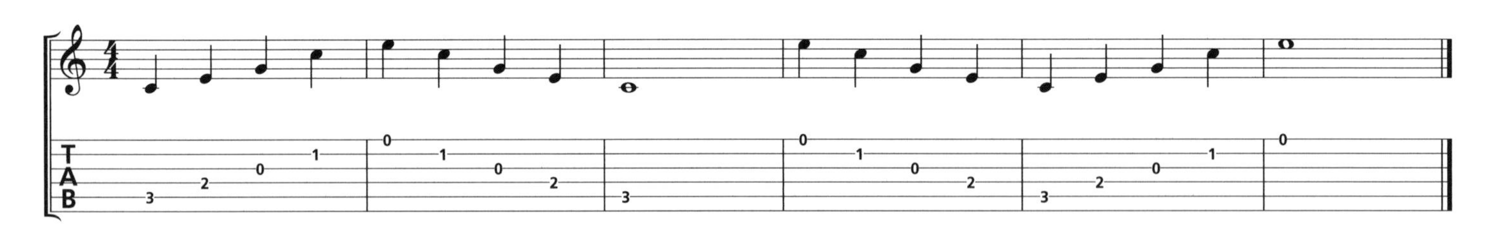

3. A minor arpeggio

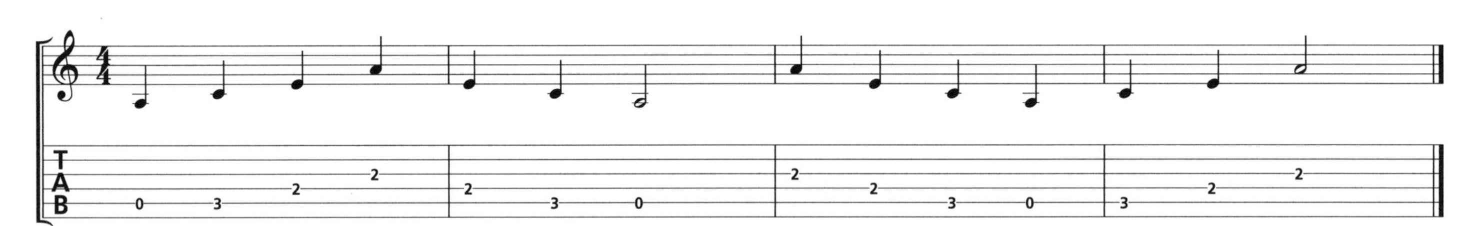

4. A minor arpeggio

Group C: Chord Voicings

In the exam you will be asked to play, from memory, your choice of one chord voicing from each of the following exercises, without the aid of a backing track or metronome. However, for practice purposes a demonstration of the chords played to a metronome click is available in the downloadable audio.

1. C major

2. A minor

Sight Reading

In this section you have a choice between either a sight reading test or an improvisation and interpretation test (see facing page).

The examiner will ask you which one you wish to choose before commencing. Once you have decided you cannot change your mind.

In the sight reading test, the examiner will give you a 4–6 bar melody in the key of C major. You will first be given 90 seconds to practise, after which the examiner will play the backing track twice. The first time is for you to practise and the second time is for you to perform the final version for the exam. For each playthrough, the backing track will begin with a one bar count-in. The tempo is ♩=60.

During the practice time, you will be given the choice of a metronome click throughout or a one bar count in at the beginning.

The backing track is continuous, so once the first playthrough has finished, the count in of the second playing will start immediately.

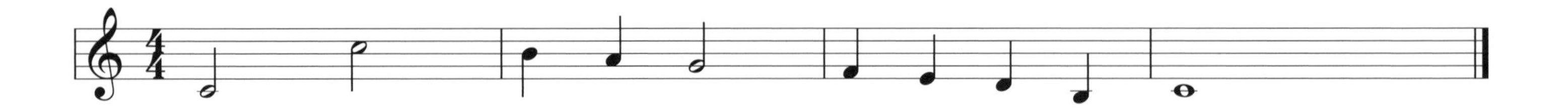

Please note: The test shown is an example. The examiner will give you a different version in the exam.

Improvisation & Interpretation

In the improvisation and interpretation test, the examiner will give you a 4–6 bar chord progression in the key of C major. You will first be given 90 seconds to practise, after which the examiner will play the backing track twice. The first time is for you to practise and the second time is for you to perform the final version for the exam. For each playthrough, the backing track will begin with a one bar count-in. The tempo is ♩= 60.

During the practice time, you will be given the choice of a metronome click throughout or a one bar count-in at the beginning.

The backing track is continuous, so once the first playthrough has finished, the count-in of the second playing will start immediately.

You are only required to improvise single note melodies.

Please note: The test shown is an example. The examiner will give you a different version in the exam.

Ear Tests

In this section, there are two ear tests:

- Melodic Recall
- Chord Recognition

You will find one example of each type of test printed below and you will need to perform both of them in the exam.

Test 1 | Melodic Recall

The examiner will play you two consecutive notes. You will need to identify whether the last note is higher or lower than the first. You will hear the test twice, each time with a one bar count-in. The tempo is ♩=95 bpm.

For this exercise, please use the word 'higher' or 'lower' in your answer.

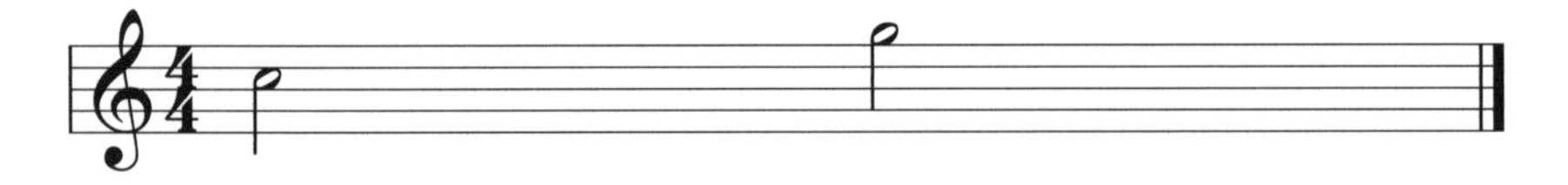

Please note: The test shown is an example. The examiner will give you a different version in the exam.

Test 2 | Chord Recognition

The examiner will play you a sequence of chords, each with a C root note. You will hear the chord sequence twice, each time with a one bar count-in. You will then be asked to identify which chord played was major and which chord was minor. The tempo is ♩=95 bpm.

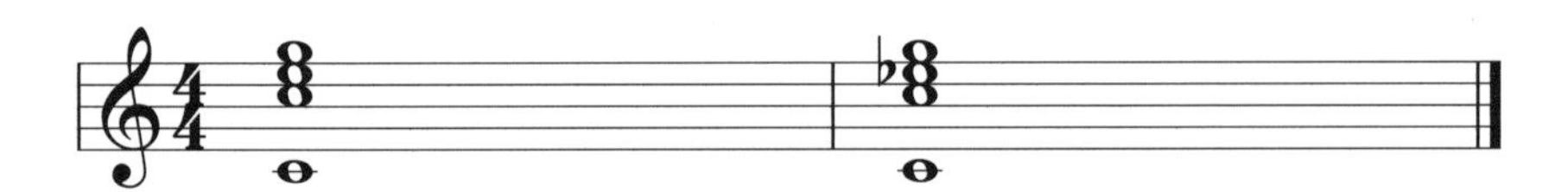

Please note: The test shown is an example. The examiner will give you a different version in the exam.

General Musicianship Questions

The final part of your exam is the General Musicianship Questions section, which features 5 questions relating to one of your choice of the performance pieces.

1. You will be asked a question relating to the harmony from a section of one of your pieces.

2. You will be asked a question relating to the melody in a section of one of your pieces.

3. You will be asked a question relating to the rhythms used in a section of one of your pieces.

4. You will be asked a question relating to the technical requirements of one of your pieces.

5. You will be asked a question relating to the genre of one of your pieces.

Entering Rockschool Exams

Entering a Rockschool exam is easy, just go online and follow our simple six step process. All details for entering online, dates, fees, regulations and Free Choice pieces can be found at *www.rslawards.com*

- All candidates should ensure they bring their own Grade syllabus book to the exam or have their KR app ready and the full book downloaded.

- All Grade 6–8 candidates must ensure that they bring valid photo ID to their exam.

- Candidates will receive their exam results (and certificates if applicable) a maximum of 3 weeks after their exam. If nothing has been received after this time then please call +44 (0)345 460 4747 or email to *info@rslawards.com*

Marking Schemes

Grade Exams | Debut to Grade 5 *

ELEMENT	PASS	MERIT	DISTINCTION
Performance Piece 1	12–14 out of 20	15–17 out of 20	18+ out of 20
Performance Piece 2	12–14 out of 20	15–17 out of 20	18+ out of 20
Performance Piece 3	12–14 out of 20	15–17 out of 20	18+ out of 20
Technical Exercises	9–10 out of 15	11–12 out of 15	13+ out of 15
Sight Reading *or* Improvisation & Interpretation	6 out of 10	7–8 out of 10	9+ out of 10
Ear Tests	6 out of 10	7–8 out of 10	9+ out of 10
General Musicianship Questions	3 out of 5	4 out of 5	5 out of 5
TOTAL MARKS	**60%+**	**74%+**	**90%+**

Grade Exams | Grades 6–8

ELEMENT	PASS	MERIT	DISTINCTION
Performance Piece 1	12–14 out of 20	15–17 out of 20	18+ out of 20
Performance Piece 2	12–14 out of 20	15–17 out of 20	18+ out of 20
Performance Piece 3	12–14 out of 20	15–17 out of 20	18+ out of 20
Technical Exercises	9–10 out of 15	11–12 out of 15	13+ out of 15
Quick Study Piece	6 out of 10	7–8 out of 10	9+ out of 10
Ear Tests	6 out of 10	7–8 out of 10	9+ out of 10
General Musicianship Questions	3 out of 5	4 out of 5	5 out of 5
TOTAL MARKS	**60%+**	**74%+**	**90%+**

Performance Certificates | Debut to Grade 8 *

ELEMENT	PASS	MERIT	DISTINCTION
Performance Piece 1	12–14 out of 20	15–17 out of 20	18+ out of 20
Performance Piece 2	12–14 out of 20	15–17 out of 20	18+ out of 20
Performance Piece 3	12–14 out of 20	15–17 out of 20	18+ out of 20
Performance Piece 4	12–14 out of 20	15–17 out of 20	18+ out of 20
Performance Piece 5	12–14 out of 20	15–17 out of 20	18+ out of 20
TOTAL MARKS	**60%+**	**75%+**	**90%+**

* Note that there are no Debut Vocal exams.

Copyright Information

Chasing Cars
(Quinn/Simpson/Lightbody/Connolly/Wilson)
Universal Music Publishing BL Limited/Universal Music Publishing Limited

Learn to Fly
(Grohl/Hawkins/Mendel)
Kobalt Music Publishing Limited/Universal Music Publishing Limited/Bug Music Ltd

Brown Eyed Girl
(Morrison)
Universal Music Publishing Limited

No Woman, No Cry
(Ford)
Blue Mountain Music Ltd

If I Were A Boy
(Gad/Carlson)
BMG Rights Management US LLC/Universal/MCA Music Limited

Yellow
(Champion/Martin/Buckland/Berryman)
Universal Music Publishing MGB Limited

mcps

BECOME A MORE CONFIDENT, EXPRESSIVE & ARTICULATE MUSICIAN

Rockschool Popular Music Theory is the essential guide for contemporary musicians, composers and educators. Whatever your instrument or musical background, our theory syllabus will equip you with the practical knowledge to become a more confident, expressive and articulate musician.

The syllabus consists of 11 finely-tuned books:

WORKBOOKS Debut to Grade 8. Each grade includes a sample paper
GUIDEBOOKS Split into two levels; Debut to Grade 5 and Grades 6 to 8

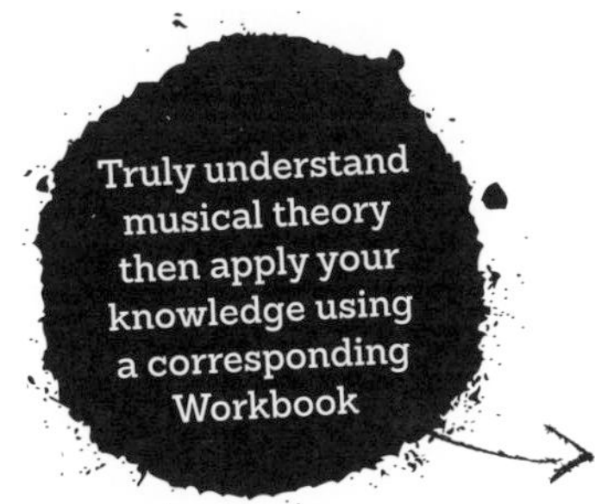

Discover everything you need to know about popular musical theory

Regardless of your current level of technical ability, or stylistic preferences, our Popular Music Theory Guidebooks will provide you with all of the information necessary to progress seamlessly through the Rockschool graded theory exams.

Acquire a hugely impressive knowledge of:

- Popular music composition
- Arranging and performance techniques
- How to read and analyse a musical score
- Specialist notation and techniques for all band instruments
- Harmony, theory and key chord progressions

The ideal preparation for students taking Rockschool theory exams

The range of Workbooks, from Debut to Grade 8, serve as grade-specific, practice texts, which enable each student to practice and apply the knowledge gained through the study of the Guidebooks, within the same structure and format of the actual Rockschool theory exams.

Each book includes sample questions for the following sections:

- Music notation
- Popular music harmony
- Band knowledge
- Band analysis

MODEL ANSWERS AVAILABLE!
Prep for each exam using the sample answers to the questions provided in your Workbook sample paper.

Download model answers
www.rslawards.com/shop

rockschool®

DIGITAL DOWNLOADS NOW AVAILABLE!

All your favourite Rockschool titles are now available to download instantly from the RSL shop. Download entire grade books, individual tracks or supporting tests to all your devices.

START DOWNLOADING NOW

www.rslawards.com/shop